# Our Hearts Can Soar

BY Eleanor Pelosi Stephenson

Illustrated by Julianna Brazill

ONION RIVER PRESS

Burlington, Vermont

Onion River Press
47 Maple Street, Suite 214
Burlington, Vermont 05401
info@onionriverpress.com

ISBN: 978-1-957184-11-1
Library of Congress Control Number: 2023900810

For

♥ Daphne  and ♥ Penelope

♥ Mommy

To Anita Brazill

My Mother and inspiration

♥ Julianna

"Mom, will you tell me the story about when your heart learned to fly?" asked the little girl.

"I would love to," replied her mother.

On the night you were born,
in the moment I first met you,
an unexpected and wonderful
magic took place.

You see, my heart, the only heart
I'd ever had,
that had only ever lived
inside my body,
grew wings where there
were none before!

And then my heart spoke to me!
It said it would no longer live only inside my body.
My heart would also live beside you.
My heart would now and forever be
in two places at all times.

So I whispered to you,
"Here is my heart. It beats
within me and also beside you.
wherever you go, it will also go.
you will never be without it."
and so...

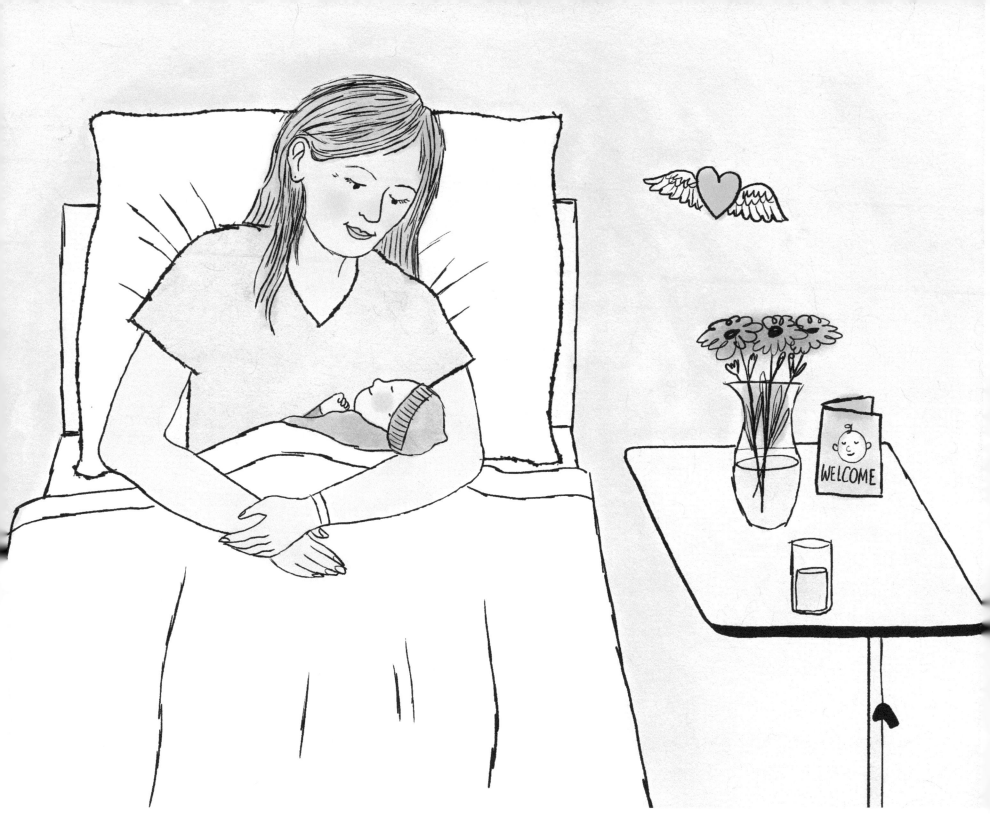

When you were a baby,
my heart fluttered around you
when you cried out for me.

I was already with you.

When you were a toddler,
my heart flew next to you as you
ventured out into the backyard,
curious and gleeful to see
how far your legs would take you.

Now, as a small child,
my heart soars above you
each day at school,
as you giggle with your friends
and ponder the day's mysteries.

In a few years, when you are
a big kid, my heart will
sail with you as you ride your
bike to the park to play
with your friends, excited
to be in the world
on your own terms,
even if only for an hour.

When you are a teenager, my heart will circumnavigate your course as you explore the bounds of your creativity and genius.

When you are a young adult, my heart will swoop about you while you forge your path as an artist, a scientist, and a humanitarian.

When you are an adult,
my heart will climb with you
as you crest ever taller peaks,
and my heart will also descend
with you slowly into the quiet valleys.

When you are an old woman,
my heart will float close by
each time you call on your wisdom
to solve, create, and care.

And so, my dear child,
when it comes to my heart,
it can do magical, incalculable physics.
My heart, like all the hearts
of parents now and before,
can multiply and soar
and time travel.

and you know what else?

So can yours.

Eleanor Pelosi Stephenson has made her home in Burlington, Vermont since 2013. It was there that she had her two daughters, who now fill every day with so much love, laughter, (exhaustion), and more love. They inspired *Our Hearts Can Soar*. When she's not writing or trying very hard at being an adult woman/mother/wife/friend, Eleanor can be found thinking about the power of love, language, and possibility.

Julianna Brazill is a Vermont-based illustrator and comic artist with a Master's in ceramics (what?) and an obsession with animals, pastries, and anything vintage. When she's not drawing, she can be found working at an antique store, wandering the great outdoors, cuddling a cat, or watching Masterpiece Mysteries.

CPSIA information can be obtained
at www.ICGtesting.com
Printed in the USA
BVHW060913040423
661733BV00003B/54